The Forgotten Toys

Teddy's Chick
Sticker Story Book

Little Hippo

The toys, Teddy and Annie,
have been forgotten by their children.
They are trying to find their way home.

*You'll find some stickers in the centre of the book.
Have fun sticking them in the right pages.
There is one sticker for every page of the story.*

Scholastic Children's Books,
Commonwealth House, 1-19 New Oxford Street,
London WC1A 1NU, UK
a division of Scholastic Ltd

London ~ New York ~ Toronto ~ Sydney ~ Auckland

First published by Scholastic Ltd, 1998

Developed from the original book The Night After Christmas,
by James Stephenson. The Forgotten Toys is an animated series produced
by Hibbert Ralph Entertainment
for Link Entertainment,
scripted by Mark Holloway,
directed by Graham Ralph and produced by Karen Davidsen.
Executive producers David Hamilton and Claire Derry.
Book illustrations by Maureen Galvani.
All rights reserved.

2 4 6 8 10 9 7 5 3 1

ISBN 0 590 19971 4

Printed in Italy by Amadeus S.p.A. - Rome

It was getting late. The toys had nowhere to stay.
"Maybe we could sleep in there," said Annie.
"It looks like a farm," said Teddy.

Annie and Teddy walked into the farm. They met a friendly cow called Brenda.

"We'll find you somewhere, dear," said Brenda.

"Thank you," said Annie.

Brenda told the toys to sleep in the hen-house, where they would be warm and snug.

"I'm not a chicken," grumbled Teddy.

The toys snuggled into the hay and slept until sunrise.

"Cockadoodledoo" crowed the cockerel, and woke them all up.
"Oi!" said Teddy, "I need my sleep!"

Teddy tried to snuggle down again but something nipped him.
"Mama!" said the chick.

"You must have hatched it," called Annie.
"I'm not your mama," said Teddy and stormed out.
The chick went after him.

Teddy tried to hide but the chick followed him everywhere.
"I've had enough!" said Teddy and locked the chick in
the hen-house.

Teddy and Annie left the farm.
  "I had to do it," said Teddy, miserably.

"I wish I hadn't shouted at her," said Teddy. But the chick wasn't far behind.

The traffic roared past and frightened the little chick.
She started to run away.

"Oh no!" shouted Annie. " We've got to catch her!"
The toys chased after the chick.

"Where is she?" said Annie. Suddenly they heard a noise.

"Mama!" said the chick. She had hidden inside an eggbox!

"Did you hear that?" asked Teddy.
"Follow that trolley!" shouted Annie.

The toys rushed at the trolley and pushed it out of the supermarket and into the street.

But the trolley raced out of control and crashed into a wall.

The eggbox and the chick were thrown into the air.
They landed in a fountain in the park below.

Teddy rushed after her.

"She's safe," said Annie.

"Thanks to me!" said Teddy.

The toys brought the little chick back home to the farm.

"Thank goodness she's safe!" said Brenda the cow.

Annie and Teddy left the farm once again. Brenda and the sheep waved goodbye.

"She was quite cute really," said Teddy.

"You're going to miss her," said Annie.